PIANO IS EASY!

by John Aschenbrenner

All you need is a piano and this book!

Put the stickers on your piano and you're ready to play!

It's Easy!

Walden Pond Press

Children's Music Books

PIANO IS EASY
ISBN # 0-9718936-1-6

Walden Pond Press
PO BOX 566 Crugers, NY 10521
www.pianoiseasy.com

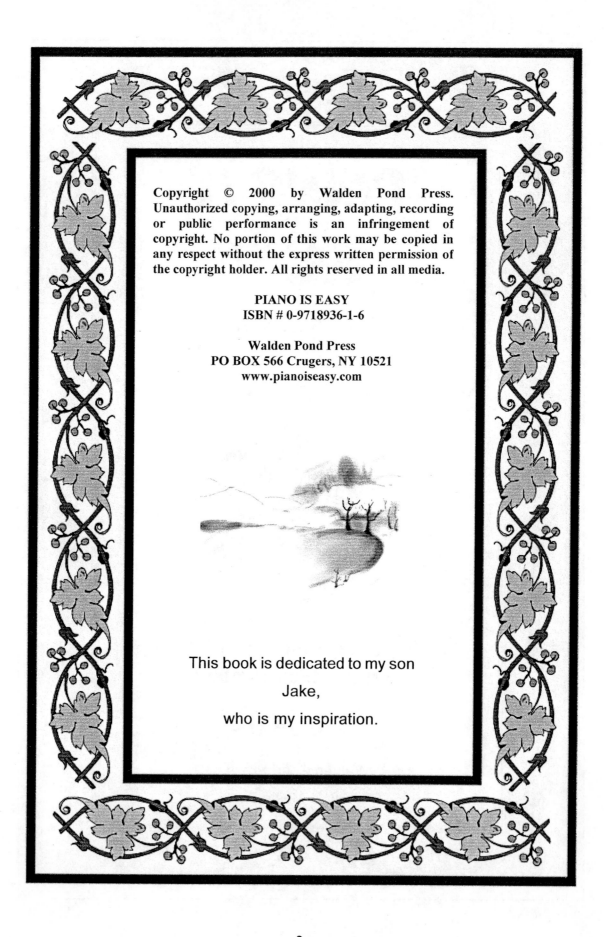

This book is dedicated to my son

Jake,

who is my inspiration.

PIANO IS EASY!

"Look, Mom, I can play piano!" For many kids, this book can be the beginning of a life-long love of music.

It's easy! Just apply the stickers provided to your piano keyboard, and you'll be ready to play the piano in a few minutes.

Easy step-by-step directions will have you playing your piano right away. You'll be amazed how easy it is to pick up the basics of music from this amazing book.

And with the Play Along Audio CD, it's like having a teacher in the room with you, guiding you along to the next step.

This book is recommended for adults and children four years and older, and an adult should supervise the application of the stickers to your piano keyboard and stay involved.

This is a perfect adult-child project. All you need is a piano and this book. Anyone can play piano, and this year it can be you and your family!

INDEX
Fun Songs for The Whole Family

INDEX
Easy Family Favorites

More Family Favorites

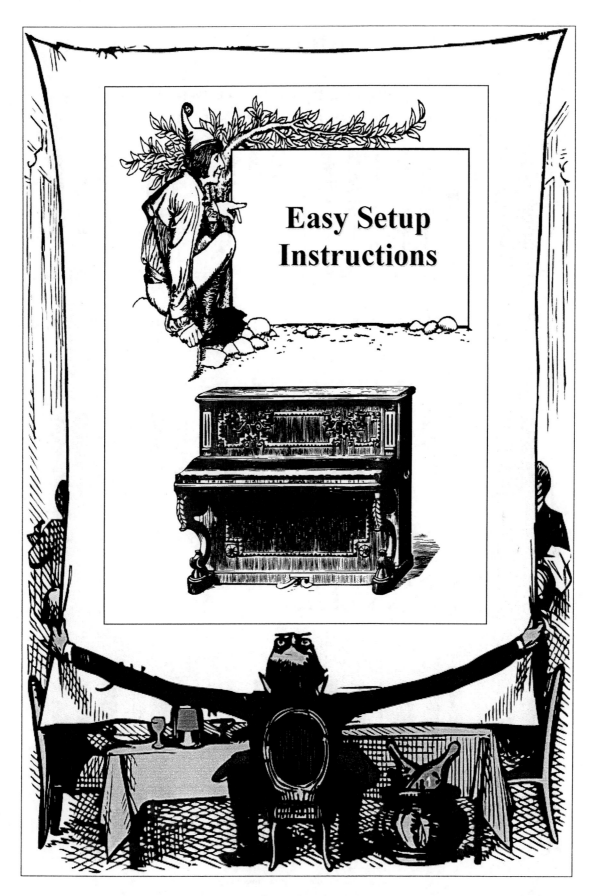

Easy Setup
Instructions

Step #1

1.1   Look at your piano. There are two colors of keys, white and black. (Only part of a full keyboard is shown.)

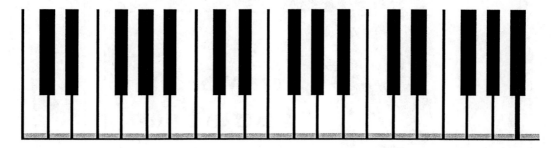

1.2   The black keys are arranged in groups of 2 and 3.

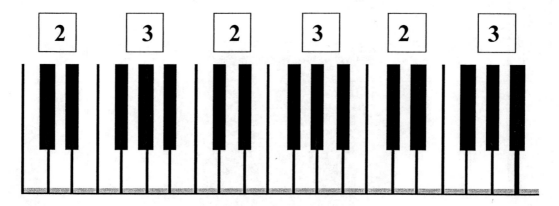

1.3   C is the name of the first white key to the left of any group of two black keys:

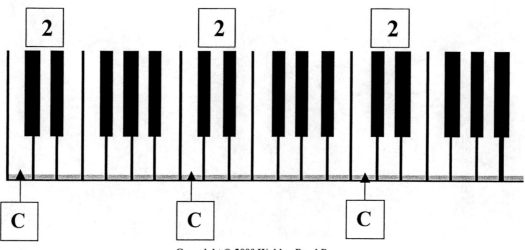

Step #2

2.1   There is a special, single white key (one of the white keys named C) <u>in the center of the piano keyboard,</u> which is specifically called "Middle C." (Only part of a full piano keyboard is shown.)

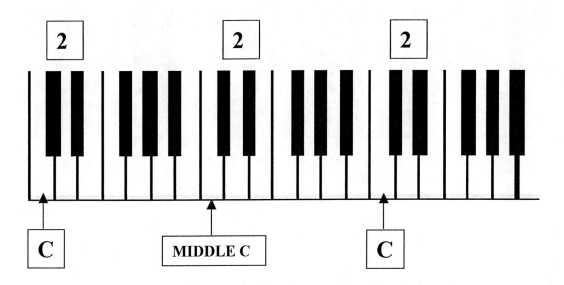

2.2   On an acoustic piano, Middle C is located in the area to the left of the manufacturer's name printed above the keys <u>in the center of the keyboard.</u> On any piano, electronic or acoustic, Middle C is the "C" which lies <u>in the center of the keyboard.</u> (Only part of a full piano keyboard is shown.)

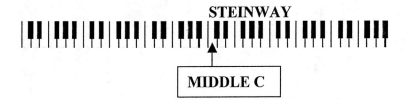

2.3   Note the location of Middle C on your piano for the next step.

Step #3

3.1   **There is a set of numbered stickers in your package. Take the sticker marked 1 (one) and place it on the white key named Middle C. (Only part of a keyboard is shown.)**

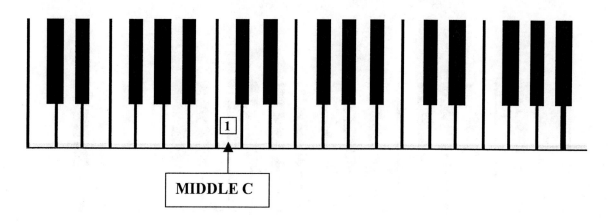

MIDDLE C

3.2   **Take the sticker marked 2 (two) and place it on the white key directly to the right of Middle C. Without skipping any white keys, finish placing the stickers (in rising numerical order) onto the white keys, moving to the right of the keyboard as you place each sticker.**

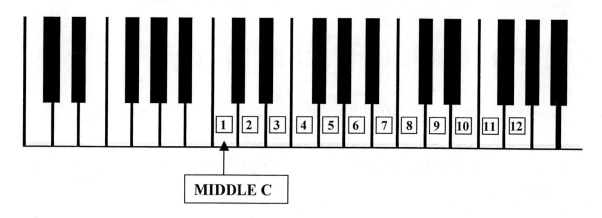

MIDDLE C

Step #4

4.1   **You should now have 12 stickers placed on the white keys of the piano, as shown below. Make sure.**

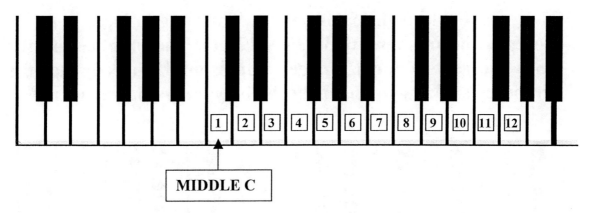

4.2   **Also make sure that the sticker numbered 8 (eight) is on the first white key named C above Middle C:**

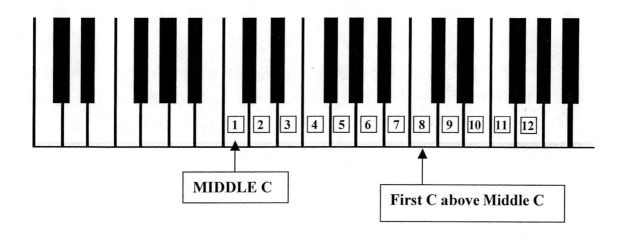

• YOU'RE READY TO PLAY THE PIANO!

Step #5

Test Flight: Play Jingle Bells

5.1   Look at the facing page. The song "Jingle Bells" is expressed in numbers: 333 333 3512 etc. The numbers on the song sheet (the facing page) correspond directly to the numbered stickers you have placed on your piano keyboard.

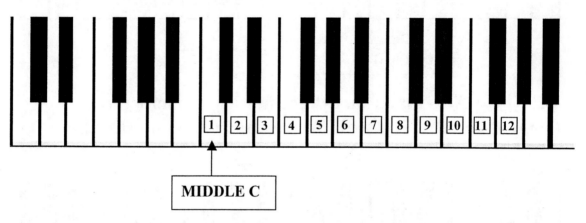

5.2   Play through the sequence of numbers: push down the numbered piano keys that correspond to the sequence of numbers on the song sheet (the facing page.) Read the numbers from left to right, like a book.

5.3   The song sheet begins with a sequence of numbers: 333 333 3512. Push down the numbered piano keys in the same order: 333 333 3512. Play the numbers until you complete the song sheet.

5.4   It doesn't matter which hand or fingers you use.

Jingle Bells

|333*|333*|3512|3***|

|4444|4333|3223|2*5*|

|333*|333*|3512|3***|

|4444|4333|5542|1***|

It's easy!

It's easy!

Fun Songs for
The Whole Family

Dashing through the snow
In a one-horse open sleigh
O'er the fields we go
Laughing all the way

Jingle Bells, Jingle Bells
Jingle all the way
Oh what fun it is to ride
In a one-horse open sleigh

Jingle Bells

|333*|333*|3512|3***|

|4444|4333|3223|2*5*|

|333*|333*|3512|3***|

|4444|4333|5542|1***|

Play Along Audio CD (Red Label) Program #s:
1. Jingle Bells Music with Teacher's voice
17. Jingle Bells Music Only

London Bridge is falling down
Falling down
Falling down
London Bridge is falling down
My fair lady

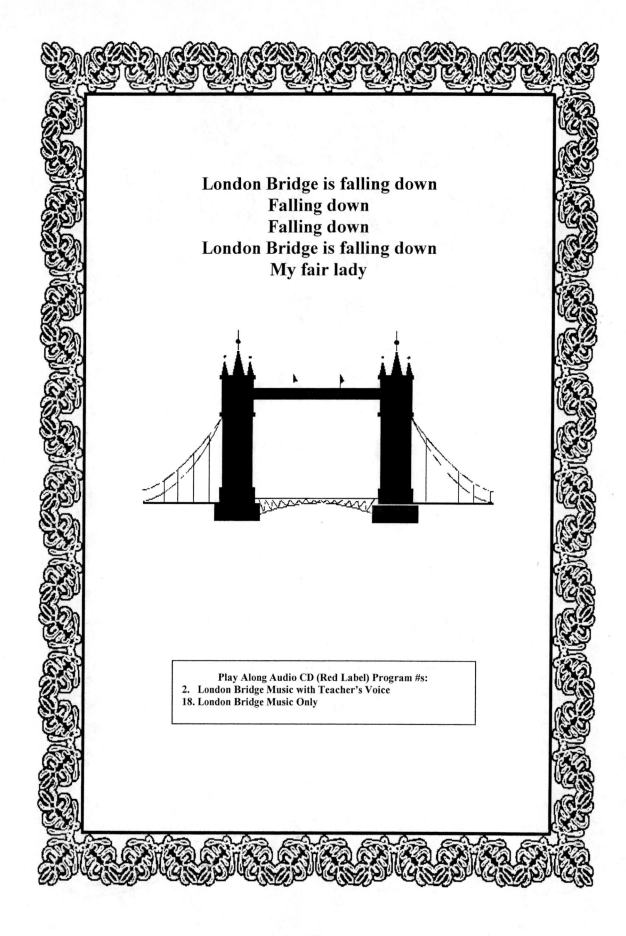

Play Along Audio CD (Red Label) Program #s:
2.   London Bridge Music with Teacher's Voice
18. London Bridge Music Only

London Bridge

|5654|345*|234*|345*|

|5654|345*|2*5*|31**|

Camptown races sing this song
Doo dah, doo dah
Camptown racetrack five miles long
Oh, doo dah day

Play Along Audio CD (Red Label) Program #s:
3. Camptown Races Music with Teacher's Voice
19. Camptown Races Music Only

Camptown Races

|5535|653*|32**|32**|

|5535|653*|2*32|1***|

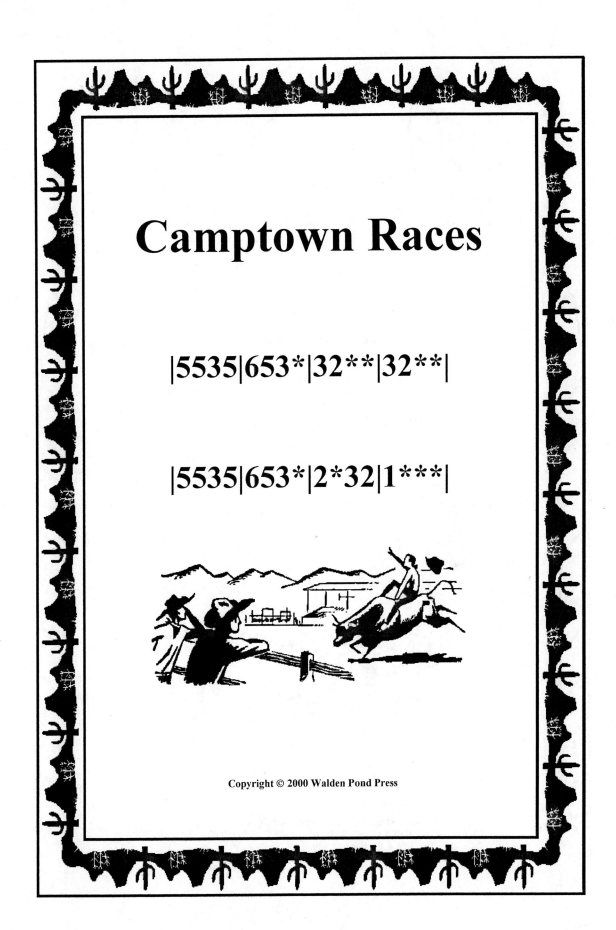

Mary had a little lamb
Little lamb
Little lamb
Mary had a little lamb
Whose fleece was white as snow

Play Along Audio CD (Red Label) Program #s:
4. Mary Had A Little Lamb Music with Teacher's Voice
20. Mary had A Little Lamb Music Only

Mary Had
A Little Lamb

|3212|333*|222*|355*|

|3212|3333|2232|1***|

Lazy Mary, will you get up
Will you get up
Will you get up
Lazy Mary will you get up
Will you get up today?

Lazy Mary

|4*4|456|8*6|4*4|

|5*5|5*6|5*3|1**|

|4*4|456|8*6|4*4|

|5*5|6*5|4**|***|

Play Along Audio CD (Red Label) Program #s:
5. Lazy Mary Music with Teacher's Voice
21. Lazy Mary Music Only

A B C D E F G
H I J K L M N O P
Q R S
T U V
W X
Y and Z
Now I know my ABC
Now I'm very proud of me

Play Along Audio CD (Red Label) Program #s:
6.   The ABC Song Music with Teacher's Voice
22. The ABC Song Music Only

The ABC Song

|1155|665*|4433|221*|

|5544|332*|5544|332*|

|1155|665*|4433|221*|

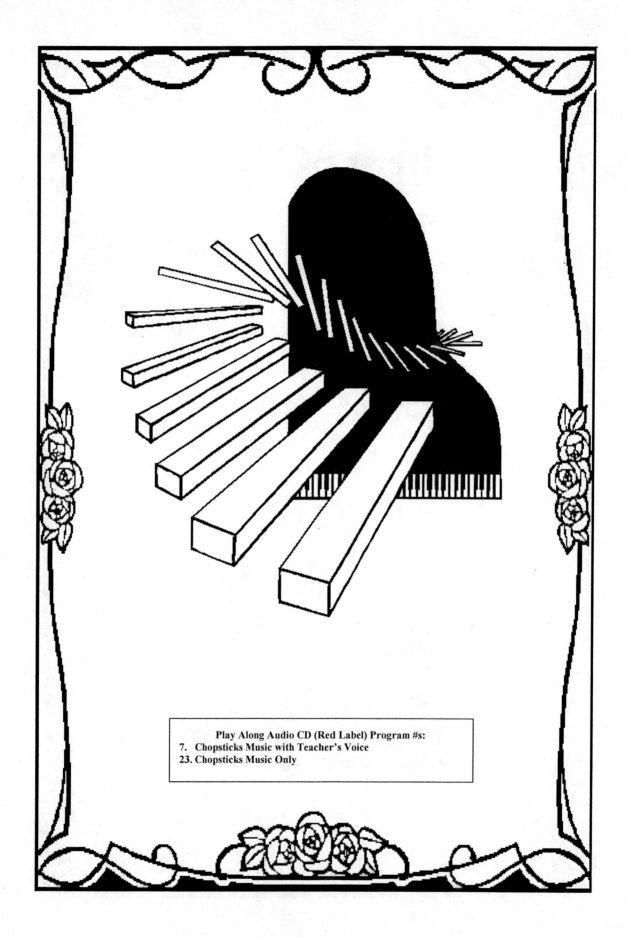

Play Along Audio CD (Red Label) Program #s:
7.   Chopsticks Music with Teacher's Voice
23. Chopsticks Music Only

Chopsticks

|555|555|555|555|

|777|767|888|876|

|555|555|555|555|

|777|767|853|1**|

Second Part at the same time:

|444|444|333|333|

|222|222|111|123|

|444|444|333|333|

|222|222|1**|***|

All around the cobbler's bench
The monkey chased the weasel
The monkey thought 'twas all in fun
Pop goes the weasel

Play Along Audio CD (Red Label) Program #s:
8. Pop Goes the Weasel Music with Teacher's Voice
24. Pop Goes the Weasel Music Only

Pop Goes the Weasel

|1*1|2*2|353|1**|

|1*1|2*4|3**|1**|

|1*1|2*2|353|1**|

|6**|2*4|3**|1**|

This train is bound for glory
This train
This train is bound for glory
This train

Play Along Audio CD (Red Label) Program #s:
9. This Train Music with Teacher's Voice
25. This Train Music Only

This Train

|44*4|6421|44**|****|

|68*8|9868|88**|****|

|68*8|9864|5444|6421|

|44*6|5421|44**|****|

Aura Lee

|5878|969*|8767|

|8***|5878|969*|

| 8 7 6 7 | 8 * * * |

(continued>>)

As the blackbird in
the spring
'Neath the willow tree
Sat and piped
I heard him sing
Sing of Aura Lee

Play Along Audio CD (Red Label) Program #s:
10. Aura Lee Music with Teacher's Voice
26. Aura Lee Music Only

| 10 10 10 * |

| 10 10 10 * |

| 10 9 8 9 |

| 10 * * * |

|10 10 11 10|

| 969*| 8767|

|8***|

Amazing Grace

|****1*|4***64|

|6***5*|4***2*|

|1***1*|4***64|

|6***5*|8*****|

(continued>>)

|****6*|8***6*|

|4***1*|2**442|

|1***1*|4***64|

|6***5*|4*****|

Amazing grace, how sweet the sound
That saved a wretch like me
I once was lost but now am found
Was blind, but now I see

Play Along Audio CD (Red Label) Program #s:
12. Ba Ba Black Sheep Music with Teacher's Voice
28. Ba Ba Black Sheep Music Only

Ba Ba Black Sheep

|1*1*|5*5*|6666|5***|

|4*4*|3*3*|2*2*|1***|

|1*11|5*55|6*66|5**5|

|4*44|3333|2*22|1***|

Ba Ba black sheep
Have you any wool?
Yes, sir, yes, sir
Three bags full

Fantasie Impromptu

|2***|3256|7***|

|9***|8*7*|6*75|

|2***|****|

(continued>>)

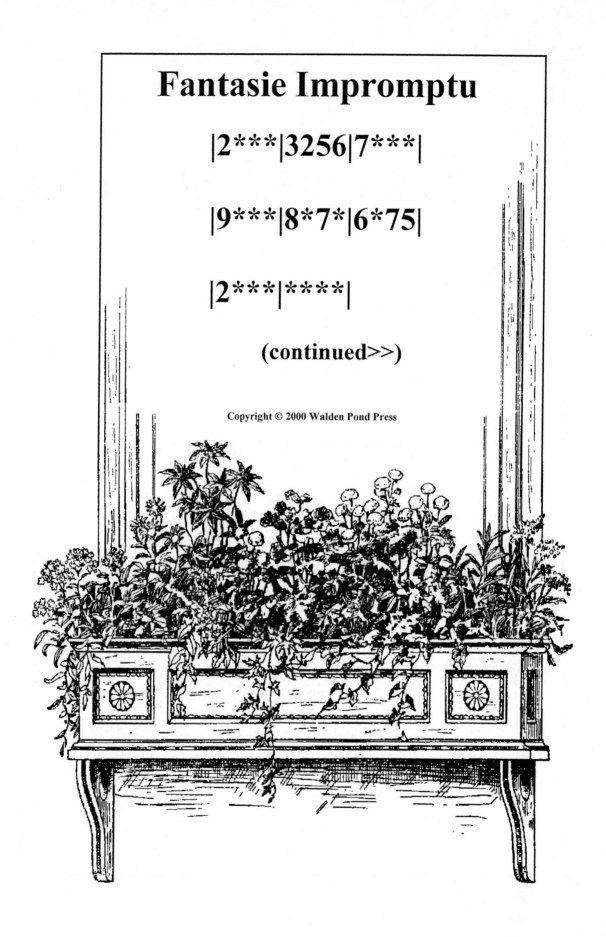

|3***|4367|8*7*|

|6*7*|5***|7**6|

|5***|****|****|

Play Along Audio CD (Red Label) Program #s:
13. Fantasie Impromptu Music with Teacher's Voice
29. Fantasie Impromptu Music Only

Barcarolle

|3*4|4*3|324|4*3|

|324|4*3|3**|***|

|3*4|4*3|324|4*3|

|324|4*3|3**|***|

(continued>>)

44

|5*6|6*7|7*8|8*7|

|7*6|6*5|5**|***|

|5*6|6*7|7*8|8*7|

|7*6|6*5|5**|***|

Play Along Audio CD (Red Label) Program #s:
14. Barcarolle Music with Teacher's Voice
30. Barcarolle Music Only

In the gloaming
Oh, my darling
When the lights are dim and low
And the quiet shadows falling
Softly come and softly go

Play Along Audio CD (Red Label) Program #s:
15. In the Gloaming Music with Teacher's Voice
31. In the Gloaming Music Only

In the Gloaming

|9**10|9*7*|9**8|8*7*|

|6*3*| 5*7*| 9**8|7***|

|9**10|9*7*|9**8|8*7*|

|6*3*| 5*7*| 7**6|5***|

Alouette, gentille Alouette
Alouette, je te plumerai
Je te plumerai la tete
Je te plumerai la tete
Et la tete, et la tete
Et la tete, et la tete

Play Along Audio CD (Red Label) Program #s:
16. Alouette Music with Teacher's Voice
32. Alouette Music Only

48

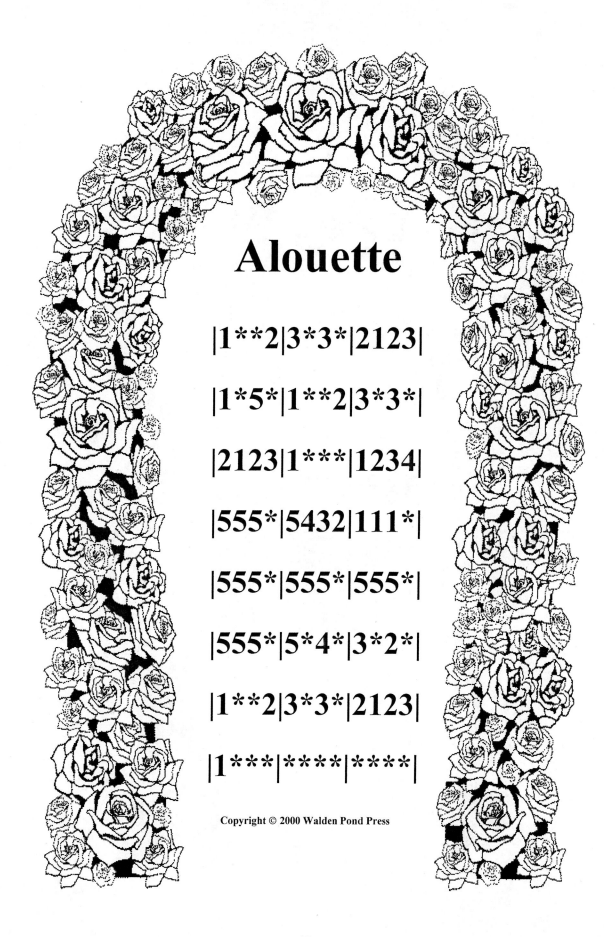

Alouette

|1**2|3*3*|2123|

|1*5*|1**2|3*3*|

|2123|1***|1234|

|555*|5432|111*|

|555*|555*|555*|

|555*|5*4*|3*2*|

|1**2|3*3*|2123|

|1***|****|****|

Easy
Family
Favorites

Oh, where, tell me where
Is your highland laddie gone?
He dwells in merry Scotland
At the sign of the blue bell

The Blue Bells Of Scotland

|**5*|8***|7*6*|

|5***|6*78|3*3*|

|4*2*|1***|**5*|

|8***|7*6*|5***|

|6*78|3*3*|4*2*|

|1***|****|****|

Her brow is like the snowdrift
Her neck is like the swan
Her face it is the fairest
The e'er the sun shone on

Annie Laurie

|**32|1**1|8**7|

|76**|***6|5**3|

|3*21|2***|**32|

|1**1|8**7|76**|

|***6|5**3|2**1|

|1***|****|****|

Vilia

|1*45|6*89|10*98|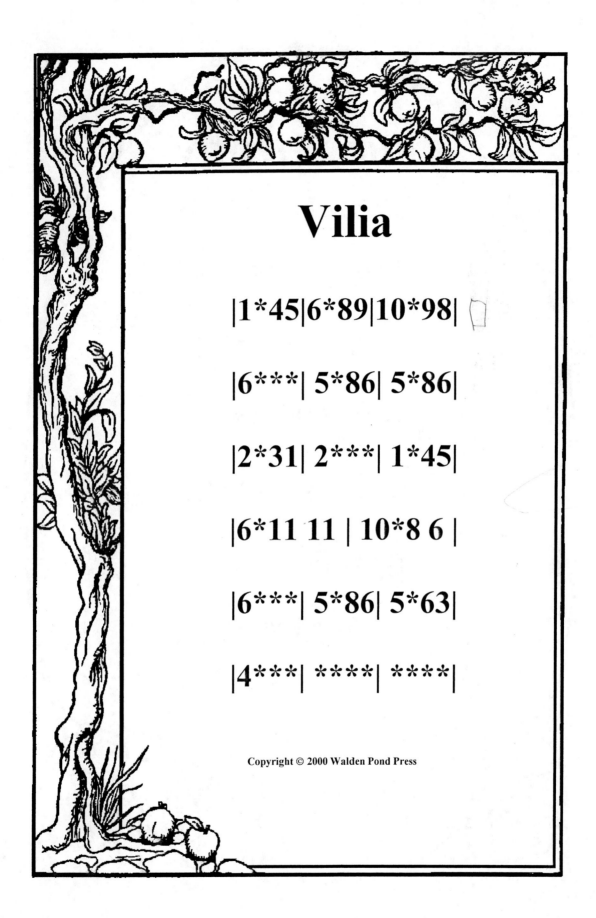

|6***| 5*86| 5*86|

|2*31| 2***| 1*45|

|6*11 11 | 10*8 6 |

|6***| 5*86| 5*63|

|4***| ****| ****|

Flow Gently Sweet Afton

|****1*|4*4*65|

|4*4*1*|2*4*2*|

|1***1*|4*4*5*|

|6*6*8*|8*6*4*|

|5***1*|

(continued>>)

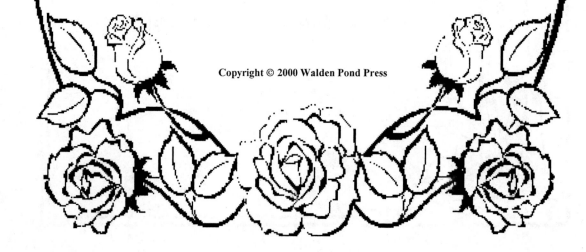

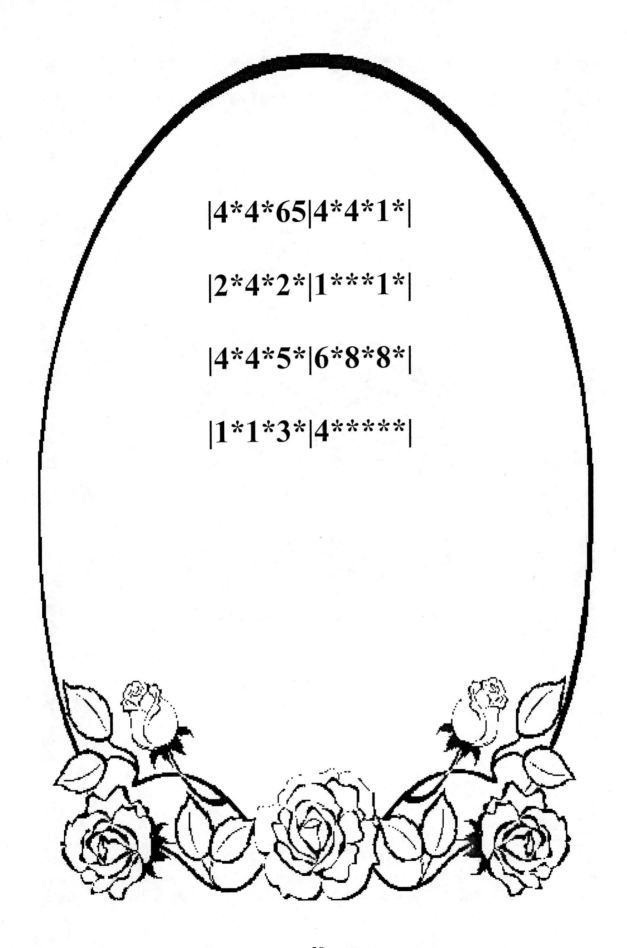

|4*4*65|4*4*1*|

|2*4*2*|1***1*|

|4*4*5*|6*8*8*|

|1*1*3*|4*****|

Listen to the mockingbird
Listen to the mockingbird
Still singing where
The weeping willows wave

Listen to the Mockingbird

|3333|3*2*|2***|****|

|2222|2*1*|1***|****|

|1***|2*2*|2*2*|2*4*|

|3*2*|3***|****|****|

|3333|3*2*|2***|****|

|2222|2*1*|1***|****|

|3***|4*6*|6*6*|6*5*|

|4*2*|1***|****|****|

I gave my love a cherry
That had no stone
I gave my love a chicken
That had no bone
I gave my love a story
That had no end
A baby when it's sleepin'
Has no cryin'

I Gave My Love A Cherry

|***1|1111|24*5|4*2*|

|1**4|5555|68*9|8*6*|

|5**5|5555|68*9|8*6*|

|5**6|5421|24*5|4*2*|

|4***|****|****|****|

Swing low, sweet chariot
Coming for to carry me home
Swing low, sweet chariot
Coming for to carry me home

Swing Low Sweet Chariot

|****|**6*|4***|**6*|

|4**4|21**|4444|668*|

|8***|**98|6***|**8*|

|4**4|21**|4444|665*|

|4***|****|

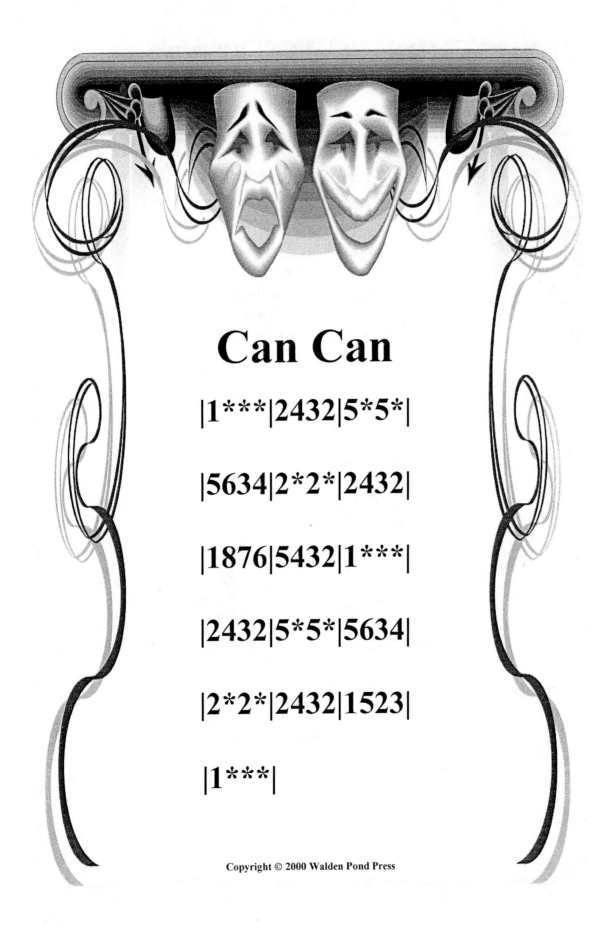

Can Can

|1***|2432|5*5*|

|5634|2*2*|2432|

|1876|5432|1***|

|2432|5*5*|5634|

|2*2*|2432|1523|

|1***|

It was many and many a year ago
In a kingdom by the sea
That a maiden there lived
Whom you may know by name
By the name of Annabel Lee

Annabel Lee

|****34|5**65*|8*7*6*|

|5**65*|1***23|4**54*|

|1**24*|3*****|****34|

|5**65*|8*7*6*|5**65*|

|1***23|4**54*|6*4*2*|

|1*****|

What shall we do
With the drunken sailor
What shall we do
With the drunken sailor
What shall we do
With the drunken sailor
Early in the morning?

The Drunken Sailor

|6*66|6*66|6*2*|4*6*|

|5*55|5*55|5*1*|3*5*|

|6*66|6*66|6*7*|8*9*|

|8*6*|5*3*|2***|2***|

In Scarlet Town where I was born
There was a fair maid dwellin'
Made every youth cry well-a-day
Her name was Barbara Allen

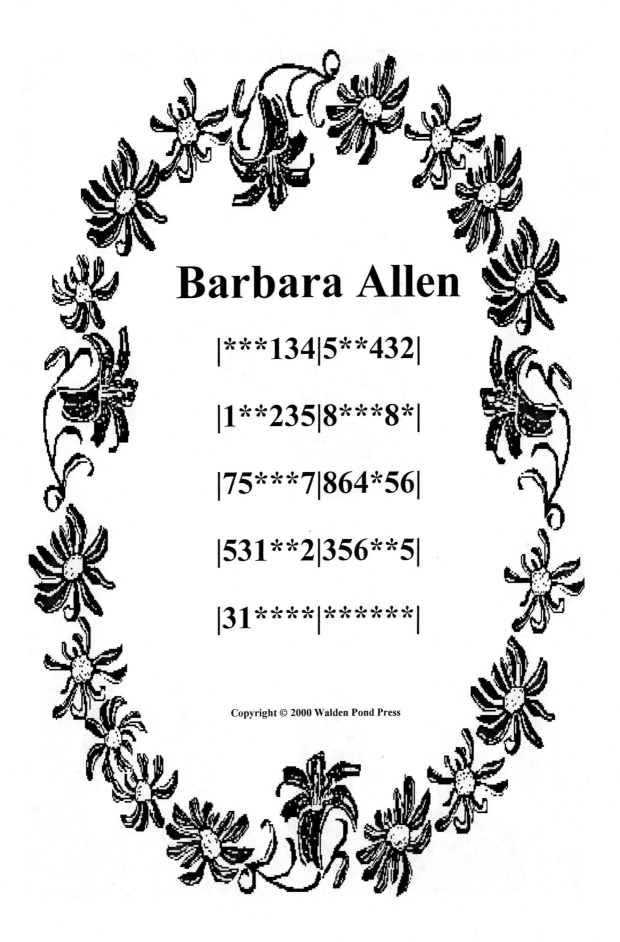

Barbara Allen

|***134|5**432|

|1**235|8***8*|

|75***7|864*56|

|531**2|356**5|

|31****|******|

Swan Lake

|10***|6789|10**8|10**8|

|10**6 | 8648 | 6***|*987|

|10***|6789|10**8|10**8|

|10**6 | 8648 | 6***|****|

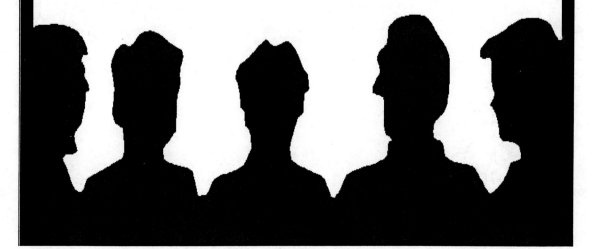

While shepherds kept their watching
O'er silent flocks by night
Behold throughout the heavens
There shone a holy light

Go Tell It On the Mountain

|7***|7653|2***|5***|

|66*6|5*6*|7676|5***|

|7***|7653|2***|5*5*|

|6*6*|756*|5***|****|

Are you sleeping
Are you sleeping
Brother John
Brother John
Morning bells are ringing
Morning bells are ringing
Ding dong ding
Ding dong ding

Frere Jacques

|1*2*|3*1*|1*2*|3*1*|

|3*4*|5***|3*4*|5***|

|5654|3*1*|5654|3*1*|

|8*5*|8***|8*5*|8***|

Tell me the tales
That to me were so dear
Long, long ago
Long, long ago
Sing me the songs
I delighted to hear
Long, long ago
Long ago

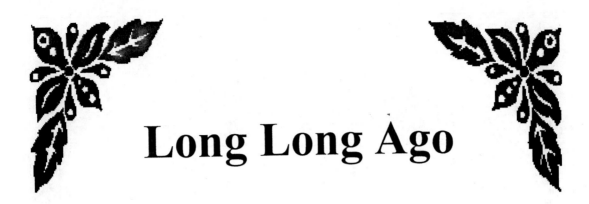

Long Long Ago

|1*12|3*34|5*65|3***|

|5*43|2***|4*32|1***|

|1*12|3*34|5*65|3***|

|5*43|2*32|1***|****|

You got to walk
That Lonesome Valley
You got to walk
It by yourself
Ain't no one here
Can walk it for you
You got to walk
That Lonesome Valley
By yourself

Lonesome Valley

| *568| 8 ***| * 10 9 8|

|65**|*878|9***|*589|

| 10 * * * | * *10 10 9 |

| 8***| *10 9 8 | 6 5**|

| * 8 8 9 | 10 10 10 10 |

|10 9 8 9| 8***|

Johnny Has Gone for a Soldier

|8*8*|7*7*|666*|

|3***|5**3|5**3|

|5*5*|1**2|3*3*|

(continued>>)

|3*21|3*6*|8***|

|888*|7*75|6***|

|6***|****|****|

There I sat
On Buttermilk Hill
Who could blame me
Cry my fill?
And every tear
Would turn a mill
Johnny has gone for a soldier

'Mid pleasures and palaces
Though we may roam
Be it ever so humble
There's no place like home

Home Sweet Home

|**12|3***|4*6*|

|5***|3*5*|4**3|

|4*2*|3***|**12|

|3***|4*6*|5***|

|3*5*|4**3|4*2*|

|1***|

I have a little draydl
I made it out of clay
And when it's dry and ready
Then draydl I shall play

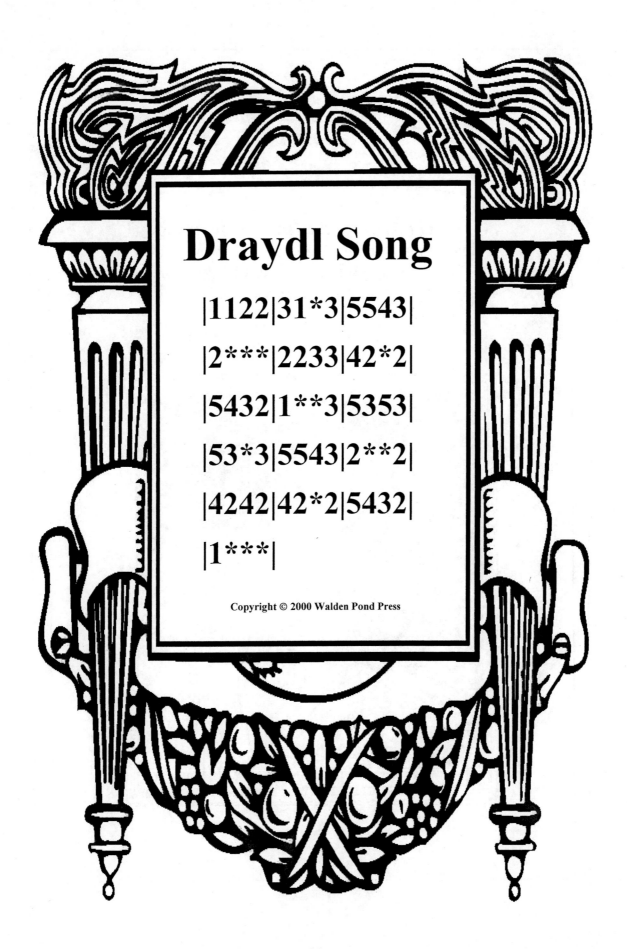

Draydl Song

|1122|31*3|5543|

|2***|2233|42*2|

|5432|1**3|5353|

|53*3|5543|2**2|

|4242|42*2|5432|

|1***|

From this valley they say you are going
I will miss your bright eyes and sweet smile
For they say you are taking the sunshine
That brightens our pathway for a while

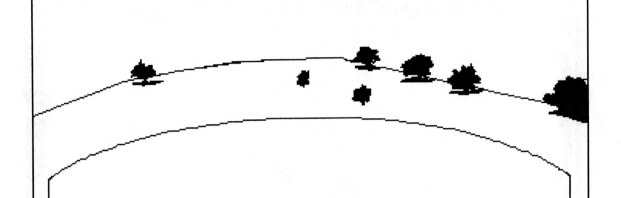

Red River Valley

|**25|7*76|5*65|35**|

|**25|7*57|9*87|6***|

|**25|7*76|5*67|98**|

|**33|2*56|7*66|5***|

A tisket, a tasket
A green and yellow basket
I wrote a letter to my love
And on the way I dropped it

I dropped it
I dropped it
And on the way I dropped it
A little boy
Picked it up
And put it in his pocket

A Tisket A Tasket

|***3|5*34|5*34|

|5536|5*33|4422|

|4422|5432|3*1*|

Skater's Waltz

|3**|5*6|6**|***|

|4**|6*7|7**|***|

|9**|8*3|5**|4*3|

|3**|2**|1**|***|

On top of Old Smokey
All covered with snow
I lost my true lover
By courting too slow

On Top of Old Smokey

|**1|135|8**|6**|

|**4|456|5**|***|

|**1|135|5**|2**|

|**3|432|1**|***|

Eensy weensy spider
Went up the water spout
Down came the rain
And washed the spider out

Eensy Weensy Spider

|1*1|1*2|3**|3*3|

|2*1|2*3|1**|***|

|3**|3*4|5**|5*5|

|4*3|4*5|3**|***|

|1*1|1*2|3**|3*3|

|2*1|2*3|1**|***|

|1*1|1*2|3**|3*3|

|2*1|2*3|1**|***|

Roses love sunshine
Violets love dew
Angels in heaven
Know I love you

Down in the Valley

|5 8 9 |10**|8**|

|***| 10 9 8|9**|

| ***| ***| 5 7 9|

|12**|12**| ***|

|11 10 9|8**|

I asked my love
To take a walk
Down beside
Where the waters flow

Banks of the Ohio

|**1*|1*3*|3***|****|

|**1*|1*3*|2***|****|

|**2*|2*3*|4***|****|

|**44|4*5*|3***|****|

|****|3*5*|5***|****|

|**33|4*5*|4***|****|

|**5*|5*4*|3***|****|

|**23|2*1*|1***|

Blow the man, bullies
Blow the man down
Hey, hey,
Blow the man down

Blow the Man Down

|565|313|565|3**|5**|6**|

| 434 | 2**|11 12 11| 9 7 9|

| 11 12 11 | 9**| 555 | 5*4|

| 323 | 1**|

The Bear Went Over The Mountain

|**1|3*3|323|4**|3*3|

|2*2|212|3**|1*1|3*3|

|323|4**|6*6|5*5|4*2|

|1**|**3|5*5|6*6|5**|

|**1|3*3|4*4|3**|**1|

(continued>>)

|3*3|323|4**|3*3|

|2*2|212|3**|1*1|

|3*3|323|4**|6*6|

|5*5|4*2|1**|

The bear went over the mountain
The bear went over the mountain
The bear went over the mountain
To see what he could see